STAND TALL

Judith Adams

Senior Authors
Carl B. Smith
Ronald Wardhaugh
Literature Consultant
Rudine Sims

Macmillan Publishing Co., Inc.
New York
Collier Macmillan Publishers
London

Macmillan Publishing Co., Inc.
866 Third Avenue, New York, N.Y. 10022
Collier-Macmillan Canada, Ltd.

Printed in the United States of America 2-Q
ISBN 0-02-121570-7

ACKNOWLEDGMENTS

Editor: *Kim Choi*

Art Direction: *Zlata Paces*

Cover Design: *Norman Gorbaty Design Inc.* Illustrators: Roberto Innocenti, pp. 6-17; Carol Taback, pp. 20-37; Charles Varner, pp. 38-39; Richard Kramer, pp. 40-53; James Foote, pp. 56-61; Stephen Tarantal, pp. 62-63; Roberto Innocenti, pp. 64-81; Richard Brown, pp. 84-87; Jack Endewelt, pp. 88-89; Larry Ross, pp. 90-99; Len Ebert, pp. 110-125.

Photo Credit: p. 58, top left, Dennis Stock; top right, Burke Uzzle; bottom, Stern.

The publisher gratefully acknowledges permission to reprint the following copy-righted material:

"Impossible, Possum" from *Impossible, Possum* by Ellen Conford. Copyright © 1971 by Ellen Conford. By permission of Little, Brown and Co.

"Soup for the King" a play adapted from *Soup for the King* by Leonard Kessler. Copyright © 1969 by Grosset & Dunlap, Inc. Published by Grosset & Dunlap, Inc.

"Always the Same" (original title "Some things I want to have different and new . . .") from *I Wonder Why* by Ruth P. Harnden. Copyright © 1971 by Ruth P. Harnden. Used by permission of Houghton Mifflin Company and Russell and Volkening, Inc.

"Undefeated" from *Street Poems* by Robert Froman. Copyright © 1971 by Robert Froman. By permission of Saturday Review Press, a Division of E. P. Dutton Co., Inc.

"Tall Tina" from *Tall Tina* by Muriel Stanek. Copyright © 1971 by Muriel Stanek. Reprinted by permission of Albert Whitman & Company.

"The Knee-High Man" from *The Knee-High Man and Other Tales* by Julius Lester. Copyright © 1972 by Julius Lester and by permission of Ronald Hobbs Literary Agency. Reprinted by permission of The Dial Press.

"Who Am I?" reprinted from *At the Top of My Voice and Other Poems* by Felice Holman. Copyright © 1970 by Felice Holman. Published by Grosset & Dunlap, Inc.

"Gordon the Goat" from *Gordon the Goat* by Munro Leaf. Copyright 1944, renewed © 1972 by Munro Leaf. Reprinted as adapted by permission of J. B. Lippincott Company.

"The Fastest Quitter in Town" adapted from *The Fastest Quitter in Town* by Phyllis Green. Copyright © 1972 by Phyllis Green. A Young Scott Book from Addison-Wesley Publishing Company.

Stand Tall

CONTENTS

5

Impossible, Possum

Ellen Conford

Randolph was a young possum. He had a special problem.

"I don't understand it," his mother said. "All possums hang by their tails and sleep upside down. Why can't you?"

"I don't know," Randolph said sadly. "I really do try hard."

"Try again," said his father. "Maybe you just need to try a little more."

"All right," sighed Randolph. He moved very slowly out onto a branch of their tree. He wound his tail around the branch, took a big breath, and let go. He didn't fall.

"He's doing it!" yelled his brother
Eugene.

"No, he's not," said his sister
Geraldine. Randolph's tail opened, and
he fell to the ground, head first.

"Dear me!" said his mother.
"Are you hurt?"

"No more than all the other times I
fell," said Randolph. "I think I'm all right."

7

"I just don't understand," his father said. "All possums know how to hang upside down."

"It's impossible—just impossible," Randolph sighed. "You might as well get used to it—I'm a flop. I can't hang by my tail."

"No, you're not a flop," said his mother kindly. "You just have to keep trying."

"But every time I try," cried Randolph, "I fall on my head. That hurts!"

"We could put a big pile of leaves under the tree," Eugene said. "Then if you fall, you will fall on something soft."

8

"*If* he falls! You mean, *when* he falls," laughed Geraldine.

"Now, now, Geraldine," said her father. "It's a very good idea. Go help your brothers find some leaves."

Randolph, Eugene, and Geraldine ran around looking for leaves. After a while, they had made a big pile of them under the branch.

"Here I go again," sighed Randolph. He climbed slowly up the tree and out onto the branch. He wound his tail around it, and let go. His tail opened, and he fell head first into the pile of leaves.

9

Again and again he tried to hang by his tail. Again and again he fell onto the pile of leaves, head first. His brother and sister went off to play. His mother and father went for a walk.

Randolph went on hanging and falling, hanging and falling. At last he gave up.

"No more," he said to himself, as he lay on his back in the leaves. "Maybe other possums can sleep upside down, but I can't. When my family goes to sleep hanging upside down on the branch, I will sleep on my pile of leaves. It's really very soft down here. Come to think of it, it's so nice I think I'll go to sleep right now." And he did.

Sap Helps

Randolph woke up to find that Geraldine and Eugene were jumping into his pile of leaves. "This is fun!" yelled Geraldine.

"It may be fun for you," Randolph sighed. "For me it's just a place to sleep." He got up and cleaned himself off. A few leaves stuck to his tail.

"I'll help you," said Eugene. He tried to pull the leaves from Randolph's tail, but the leaves wouldn't come off. Geraldine pulled hard and came away with a leaf in her paw.

"Don't!" said Randolph. "That hurts."

"Look!" Geraldine said. Something was slowly falling from the end of the branch.

"Sap!" she said. "You got sap on your tail, and that's why the leaves stuck to it."

11

Randolph stopped picking
leaves from his tail. "Why didn't
I think of this before?" he cried.
"If sap makes leaves stick to my
tail, maybe it will make my tail
stick to the branch."

Randolph held his tail under the sap.
Then he ran up the tree, and wound
his tail around a branch. He held on
with his paws until he was sure
the sap was sticking.

Then he opened
his paws and hung down.

He didn't fall!

12

"Look at me!" he yelled. "Look, everyone!" His mother and father came running.

"Good for you, Randolph!" said his father. "You see, you just had to keep trying."

"I don't think it was that," said Randolph. "I think it was the sap."

"But how is he going to get down?" asked Geraldine.

"I never thought of that," Randolph said.

"It's all right," his mother said kindly. "We will just unwind your tail for you when you want to come down."

"Well, don't unwind it now. I think I'll just hang here for a while," said Randolph. "I might even take a little nap."

From then on, Randolph held his tail under the sap before the possums went to sleep. His mother had to unwind it for him when he woke up.

But one day, Randolph could not find any sap on the tree.

"What will I do now?" he cried.

"Randolph," said his father, "winter is coming. In the winter, sap dries up. You must try to hang like the rest of us, without sap."

"It's impossible," said Randolph to himself. "I just can't do it without sap."

Just then, Geraldine ran over to him. "Look," she said, "I found more sap, and I put it on this leaf. Would you like me to rub it on your tail?"

"That's very nice of you, Geraldine," said Randolph, and he held out his tail.

Then he ran up the tree. "Geraldine found some more sap," called Randolph. He had opened his paws and was hanging by his tail. "It works! Thank you, Geraldine."

Everyone came over to look. Then Geraldine yelled, "Randolph, you're doing it! Look at Randolph! He's doing it!"

"Sure he's doing it," said Eugene. "He can always do it with the sap on his tail."

"No, no, no!" cried Geraldine, jumping up and down. "It wasn't sap, it was water! I put water on the leaf. It was a trick!"

"Water?" cried Randolph.

"That was a mean trick, Geraldine," said Eugene.

"But he is hanging by his tail!" Geraldine said. "By himself! With no sap!"

"Randolph, this is wonderful! I'm so proud of you!" said his mother.

"I can do it! I can do it!" Randolph yelled.

"You just had to think you could do it," said his father.

16

"You just needed a tricky sister," said Eugene.

"You mean a smart sister," said Geraldine.

The possums were so happy that they ran out onto the branch and sang "He's a Jolly Good Possum" to Randolph, who was hanging upside down by his tail.

And no one sang louder than Randolph.

Hot Soup

Some words are describing words. They tell how
things look, feel, smell, sound or taste. Here's
a game for you. It's called Hot Soup, Cold Soup.
One of you says a name word, like soup.
Another says two describing words that could
go with the name word, like hot soup, cold soup.
Soup could be hot or cold. What else could it be?

Snake.

Slithery
snake,
slippery
snake.

Cold Soup

Name Words

leaf ⟶

possum ⟶

baby ⟶

cake ⟶

clown ⟶

forest ⟶

giant ⟶

shoes ⟶

thunder ⟶

soap ⟶

rock ⟶

song ⟶

kitten ⟶

mouse ⟶

Describing Words

dry leaf, green leaf

20

SOUP FOR THE KING

A Play

Adapted from a story by Leonard Kessler

THE PLAYERS

King	Tailor
Queen	Tailor's Wife
Page	Tailor's Son
Royal Cook	Soldier
Some Cooks	

ACT I

TIME: Long ago

PLACE: The dining room in the Royal Palace

(The king and queen are sitting at a table. A page looks on.)

King: What's for supper?

Queen: It's soup again. *(She sighs.)* Don't you think we could have other things to eat sometimes?

King: I love soup. It's what I want.

Queen: But soup every day? Hot soup, cold soup, new soup, old soup. Soup for breakfast, soup for lunch, and soup for supper. Soup! Soup! Soup!

King: I love soup. It's what I want.

Queen: Then we shall have soup for supper. *(She sighs.)* Page, please bring the soup.

(Page brings the soup. The king and queen eat.)

King: Mm-m-m-m! I love soup.

ACT II

TIME: The next morning

PLACE: The kitchen in the Royal Palace

(The royal cook is holding a spoon over a big pot. The queen comes in.)

Queen: What are you cooking there, royal cook?

Cook: The royal soup for lunch.

(The queen takes the spoon from the cook and tastes the soup.)

Queen: Don't you think it needs a little more salt?

Cook: More salt? *(He tastes the soup.)*
No, it's just right.

(The queen takes another taste.)

Queen: It needs more salt, I tell you.

Cook: Royal Queen, I am the king's soup cook
and the best cook in all the land.
I know how the king likes his soup.

Queen: Well, I am the king's wife. I eat
soup with the king every day. I know
how the king likes his soup. Put in
more salt.

Cook: Very well. If that's how it is,
you cook the soup. I'm leaving for good!

*(The royal cook takes off his hat and apron,
and hands them to the queen. He walks out.)*

Queen: Dear me! I can't cook. There will be
no soup for lunch. What shall I do?

ACT III

TIME: Lunchtime

PLACE: The Royal Dining Room

(The king and queen are at the table. A page looks on.)

King: What's for lunch?

Queen: Lunch? Let me see. Mm-m-m-m. How about a nice jelly sandwich?

King: How about soup?

Queen: Dear me! Mm-m-m-m. A cold ham sandwich would be very good.

King: No, thank you. I don't want a sandwich.
I want soup.

Queen: There is no soup.

King: No soup? What did you say?

Queen: There is no royal cook.
He walked out.

King: What? No cook? No soup? Well then,
we must find a new cook. Page, go
to the town and find some cooks. Tell them
all to bring their best soup to the palace.

Page: I will do as you say. *(He goes out.)*

ACT IV

TIME: The same day

PLACE: A poor tailor's house outside the town

(The tailor and his wife and their son are sitting at a table.)

Tailor: What's for lunch today?

Wife: Soup.

Tailor: Soup?

Son: Soup again?

Tailor: All we ever eat is soup. I can't look at soup again.

Wife: But we are too poor to buy any other kind of food. That's all there is to eat.

Tailor: I won't eat soup. I want meat!

(The wife thinks for a while.)

Wife: Son, take this pot of soup to town. See if you can sell it, and buy some meat for supper. Now go right away. And remember, be good.

Son: Yes, Mother. I'll do as you say, but who would want to buy this soup?

(He goes out.)

ACT V

TIME: That afternoon

PLACE: Outside the Royal Palace

(There is a line of cooks outside the palace door. Each one has a pot of soup. The son comes by with his pot of soup.)

Soldier: What have you there, boy?

Son: A pot of soup.

Soldier: Then get in line with the other cooks.

Son: But…but…

Soldier: Go on, get in line.

(The son goes to the end of the line. A page comes out of the palace.)

Page: The cooks may now go into the Royal Dining Room. The king will taste each cook's soup.

(The cooks and the tailor's son go inside.)

31

ACT VI

TIME: A little later

PLACE: The Royal Dining Room

(The king and queen are waiting. The king has a big gold spoon. One by one, the cooks come in and put their soup down on the table.)

Cook One: Try my soup, Your Majesty.

(The king tries the soup.)

King: No taste!

Cook Two: My soup is very tasty, Your Majesty.

(The king tries the soup.)

King: Undercooked!

Cook Three: My soup is not undercooked,
Your Majesty.

(The king tries the soup.)

King: Overcooked!
Is there no good soup cook in all the land?

Queen: Dear me! Dear me!

(The king walks over to the tailor's son.)

King: Well, what have we here? A little cook?

(The king laughs and tries the son's soup.)
Mm–m–m–m. Very, very good. *(He takes
another taste.)* What wonderful soup!

Son: But this is just everyday potato soup.

King: But it is potato soup fit for
a king! I want you to be
the new royal soup cook. Page, bring
the royal cook's hat and apron.

Son: But…but…

King: But, what?

Son: I can't cook.

King: You can't cook? Then who made
this wonderful soup?

Son: It was my mother.

King: Then we shall send for your mother right away. Soldier, go and find this boy's mother and bring her to the palace.

Soldier: Yes, Your Majesty. *(He goes.)*

King: *(To the tailor's son)* And while we are waiting, you and I and the queen will eat this wonderful soup!

(They sit and eat. The soldier comes back with the tailor and the tailor's wife.)

Wife: My son eating soup with the king!

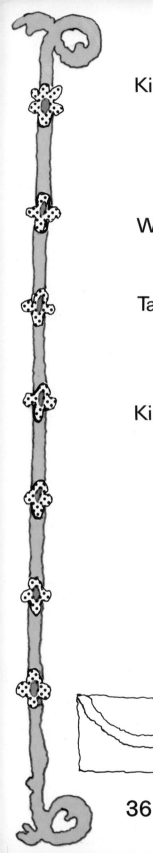

King: My dear woman, your soup is the most wonderful soup I have ever tasted. Will you live in the palace and be the royal soup cook?

Wife: Me? The royal soup cook? Why... why...yes, Your Majesty!

Tailor: Soup, soup, soup! Even in the Royal Palace, is that all there is to eat?

King: What would you like to eat?

Tailor: I'll eat anything. Anything but soup. No soup for me!

King: Very well. You may live here and eat meat and potatoes or whatever you like.

Tailor: Why, thank you, Your Majesty!

Queen: How nice! There will be other things to eat in the palace from now on.

King: But I'll eat soup! Hot soup, cold soup, new soup and old soup, bean soup, green soup, soup with beets, and soup with rice. All kinds of soup!

Always the Same

Some things I want to have different and new,
Like clothes, or a book, or a game,
But when it comes to what I eat
I want it always the same.

I know exactly what I like,
And it agrees with me,
So I can eat it every day
Very contentedly.

Nothing's wrong with my appetite.
In fact, if you ask me,
People who want all different meals
Aren't hungry as they should be.

Or maybe they keep on hoping
They'll sometime find a treat
That they like just as much as I
Like what I always eat.

—Ruth Harnden

39

Something to Share

Francisco Jimenez

Anita sat quietly. She listened to John as he shared his rock collection with the class. When he was done, all the boys and girls clapped.

"That was very nice, John," said Mrs. Green. "Now, let me see. Who's going to share next time? Ben shared his paper dragons. Betsy shared her pretty dolls from Japan, and Andy shared his collection of toy cars." Mrs. Green looked around the class. "Oh, yes, Monday will be Anita's turn to share something with us."

When Anita heard this, she wanted to hide. She knew her turn was coming, but not this soon. Later, when the class went to the playground, Anita did not want to play. She sat on the grass.

"What's the matter, Anita?" asked her friend Kim. "You're so quiet. Do you feel sick?"

"No, I'm fine," said Anita. "I just don't know what I'm going to share with the class on Monday. I've been thinking about it for a long time."

"Today is only Friday," said Kim. "You have two more days to think of something."

"I know," said Anita. "But that isn't very long."

When Anita got home that afternoon, her grandma and her little brother Paco were in the living room.

"How was school, Anita?" asked Grandma.

"Fine, Grandma," said Anita.

Paco ran up and gave Anita a hug. "Will you play with me?" he asked.

Anita smiled. "Not now, Paco. I have to help Grandma clean the living room and make dinner before Mama and Papa come home from the store."

"Are you going to help Mama and Papa at the store tomorrow?" asked Grandma.

"Oh, yes," said Anita.

The living room was clean and dinner was ready when Mama and Papa came home. The whole family sat at the table to eat.

Anita was quiet for a while. Then she looked at Papa and said, "Papa, can I stay home Monday? I can help you at the store."

"You can help us at the store tomorrow," said Papa. "On Monday you have to go to school."

"Papa is right," said Mama. "But why don't you want to go to school on Monday?"

Anita looked down. She thought of how the class had clapped for John. She didn't know what to say.

"You don't have to tell us if you don't want to, but maybe we can help you," said Papa.

Anita wanted to tell them, but she decided to wait. She wanted to think of something to share on her own.

When Anita went to bed that night, she couldn't sleep for a while. "I will have to think of something tomorrow," she thought as she fell asleep at last.

Anita's Idea

The next day after breakfast,
Papa, Mama, and Anita drove down
Los Angeles Street to the store.

Anita saw the big sign over the door:

All morning Anita helped her Mama
and Papa clean the shop. But work did
not stop her from thinking, "What will I
share on Monday?"

Late in the morning, Anita saw
John and his mother coming into
the store.

"Anita!" said John. "I didn't know you worked here."

"This is our store," said Anita.

"Wow!" said John. "Look at all the great toys and things you have here. Where did you get these?"

"All these things are made in Mexico," said Anita's papa. "They are sent here to Los Angeles by truck."

John picked up something that looked like a ball. "What is this?" he asked.

"That is a balero," said Anita. "Haven't you ever seen one before?"

"No, never," said John. "This is the first time I've seen any of these things."

"Really?" said Anita. She thought for a while. Then she almost yelled, "I have something to share!"

"You mean with our class?" said John.

"Yes," said Anita. "I'm going to take this balero and some of these things to share in class."

"That's a great idea," said John. "Will you show us how to play with the balero?"

"Sure," said Anita. "I'll show everyone on Monday."

Monday morning Anita looked very pretty when she walked into the classroom. Her jet black eyes were very bright.

When sharing time came, Mrs. Green looked over at Anita. "It's Anita's turn to share today," she said.

Anita got up and looked at the door. She smiled and said out loud, "You may come in now, Papa." Papa walked in with a box of Mexican things from the store.

"This is my papa," said Anita. "His name is Mr. Perez. He's going to show you many nice things from Mexico." All the boys and girls clapped.

"Hello, everyone," said Papa. "I'm happy to be here."

49

"Show us how to play with the balero," John called out.

Anita's Papa picked up the balero from the box.

"This is a balero," he said. "Many children play with baleros in Mexico. The balero has two parts. It has a top with a hole in it and a stick. The top hangs from the stick on a string. You have to flip the top and catch it with the stick. The stick goes into the hole in the top part when you catch it."

Mr. Perez showed the class how to
flip the balero. Some of the boys and
girls took turns, too. Then Anita took a
piggy bank from the box.

"This piggy bank is made of clay," said Anita. "It is painted red, green, white, and brown. Boys and girls in Mexico keep their money in piggy banks like this one."

Then Mr. Perez took something small out of the box.

"This is a candy lion," he said. "We make other animals like donkeys, coyotes, and horses out of candy, too. They are very good."

52

Mr. Perez and Anita showed many more things from the store. Then Mr. Perez said, "Now, I'm going to give each one of you some Mexican candy." The whole class clapped.

Anita was very happy. She shared not only many nice things from Mexico, but she also shared her papa. She was very proud.

My Farm

Come now and see my farm for it is beau - ti - ful.

Come now and see my farm for it is beau - ti - ful.

El per - ri - to sounds like this: Bow Wow!

El per - ri - to sounds like this: Bow Wow!

Bi - en ven-i-dos, bi - en ven-i-dos, ve-nid, ve-nid, ve-nid.

Bi - en ven-i-dos, bi-en ven-i-dos, ve-nid, ve-nid, ve-nid.

Children who live in Mexico or Puerto Rico speak Spanish. Here is a song with some Spanish words. *El perrito* means *the dog. Bien venidos venid, venid, venid* means *welcome, welcome, come, come, come.* Sing the song using the other animal names, too.

A Special Tree
Judith Adams

Do you know the best place for a tree to grow? A tree grows best where it can get what it needs to live.

What does a tree need? Like all green plants a tree needs soil, water, minerals, clean air, and sunlight.

The tree's roots grow down into the soil. Soil has important minerals and water that the tree needs. The minerals and water go into the tree through its roots. They move up the tree, and into the leaves. Air and sunlight help the leaves to turn the minerals and water into food for the tree.

What places have the things that a tree needs? The green countryside? A park? A busy city street?

A city street is not a very good place for
most trees to grow. Remember the things a
tree needs: Soil, clean air, and sunlight.

Soil: There is very little soil and lots of hard
pavement in the city.

Clean air: City air is not very clean because
of all the cars.

Sunlight: Tall city buildings keep out a lot of
sunlight.

Only very strong trees can grow in the city without special help. The **ailanthus** is such a tree. Ailanthus trees line city pavements everywhere.

The ailanthus tree can grow as tall as a building. Its roots don't take up much room, so it doesn't need a lot of soil. Ailanthus roots grow close to the top of the ground so they can take in every bit of rain. City sunlight is good enough for the ailanthus tree, and city air doesn't hurt it at all.

The ailanthus has long branches and lots of pointed little leaves. In the fall, long, red-brown wings hang from the tree. The seeds of the tree are in the wings.

No one has to plant the ailanthus seed for it to grow into a new tree. The wind takes the wing-like seeds through the air. They grow wherever they land—even in cracks in the pavement.

If you find an ailanthus seed, plant it in a pot of earth, water it, and put it in the light. After a while, you will have your own, very tiny ailanthus tree.

61

Undefeated

A little square of earth
The sidewalk forgot to cover.
 Lost.
 Alone.
Until weeds start coming up.

—*Robert Froman*

63

Tall Tina

Muriel Stanek

When Tina was little, everyone at home
called her Tiny Tina. But as she grew
taller and taller and went to school, it
was just Grandma who still called
her Tiny Tina.

"Tiny, please find my
green pocketbook,"
Grandma would say.

"Here it is, Grandma,"
Tina would call.
"Right up here on the shelf."

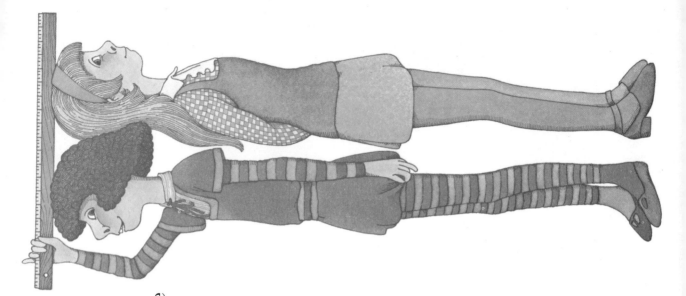

That would make Grandma smile. She would say, "My Tiny Tina is getting tall, and that's fine. There are lots of tall people in our family."

That was so. Most of Tina's family were tall. And Tina liked that. She was proud to look like one of the family.

When Tina's father put Tina and her big sister Maria back to back one day, he said, "Well, what do you know! Tina, you are as tall as Maria."

Tina liked being tall when she and her mother went shopping for new things for Tina. "Let's look at the coats for school-girls," Mother said. "Coats for little girls are too small for you now."

At school, no other girl in her class was as tall as Tina. Most of the time, this was fine with Tina. Miss Smith would say, "Tina, please get the paper from the top shelf."

"Not everyone can do that," Tina would say to herself, as she took the paper from the shelf.

66

When the class had a spring play, Miss Smith picked Tina to be a tree. Tina thought it might be fun to be one of the little birds. But on the day of the play, Tina was happy that she was a tree. She had on a tall hat that made of leaves, and she put her hands way out to make them look like branches. There were other trees, but no tree in the play was as tall as Tina. The music played, and Tina shook her branches over everyone. It was fun.

But sometimes Tina did wish she were not so tall. She didn't like to sit in the last seat in her row.

One morning Tina tried to move up three places. Miss Smith saw her and said, "Tina, you are too tall for that seat. Ben can't see over your head."

Tina walked slowly back to her old seat at the back of the room.

At home, because Tina was so tall, everyone wanted her to act more like Maria. "You are too big to be so silly," her father said when she laughed too much.

"You are too big to cry," her mother said when Tina cut her hand.

Just Grandma still thought of Tina as a little girl. "Tiny Tina," Grandma would say, "come and sit on my lap."

Tina would be happy to have someone to hold her. But when Grandma tried to rock her, Tina's long legs hit the floor. So, after a while, Tina would get down on the floor and sit with her head on Grandma's lap.

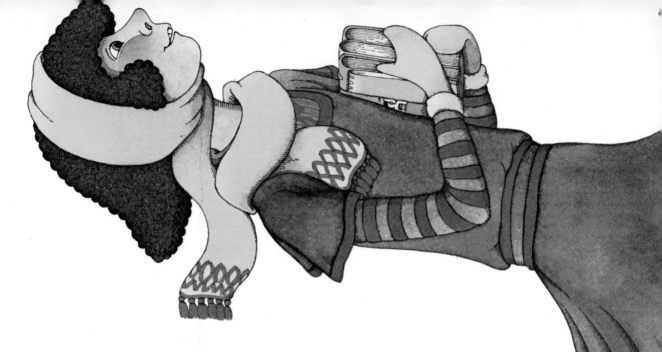

String Bean Tina

One day a new boy called Rico moved in on Tina's street. He was in her class at school. He was a short boy, but he still looked older than the other children.

In school, when Rico saw Tina looking his way, he made a face at her. When the other children walked out of the room, Rico put his foot out and made Jay fall. Two days after that, on the way home from school, Rico yelled, "Tina is a string bean—String Bean Tina!"

Some of the children laughed. Then someone called, "Tall Tina! Look at Tall Tina!"

Tina ran home without looking back at any of the children who were making fun of her.

Next morning there was a paper on Tina's seat. It said, "Tina is a ___" and there was a drawing of a giant.

Tears came into Tina's eyes. "I can't help it if I'm tall," she said to herself. She tried to hide her long legs under her seat.

Going home from school, Tina stopped to look at herself in a bakery window. Then she saw Rico. He was calling, "Tall Tina! String Bean Tina!"

71

Tina ran for home as fast as she could.

"I hate being tall," Tina told herself. "I have to look short." She tried walking without standing up as straight as she could.

"How come you aren't standing up straight?" her sister Maria asked.

"I have to look short," Tina said.

"Who cares if you are tall? Mother and Father are tall. They don't care," Maria said.

But Tina did care. She couldn't help it. She wanted to look short. She began to think everyone was laughing at her because she was tall. She didn't stand up straight when she was in school.

One afternoon when Tina was walking home, she turned around and saw Rico behind her. She ran as fast as she could for a big fence. She got behind the fence and peeked out.

As Rico came closer, she saw that he was not running after her at all. Two older boys were running after *him*! Then Rico fell, and hit his nose so hard it was bleeding.

While Tina watched, the big boys ran up and laughed at Rico. He had his hand to his nose and tears ran down his face.

"Crybaby!" the boys yelled before they ran off.

Tina stayed behind the fence until the big boys had gone. She was all ready to laugh and say, "Good, Rico! Now you know what it's like to have someone make fun of you."

But, as Tina came over to Rico, she didn't yell at him after all. She was surprised—she felt sorry for Rico! She gave him her handkerchief for his nose.

Slowly he got up. Tina and Rico walked down the street together without saying a word.

They stopped at Rico's house. His nose had stopped bleeding. Rico gave Tina back her handkerchief. "Want to see my new kitten, Tina?" Rico asked.

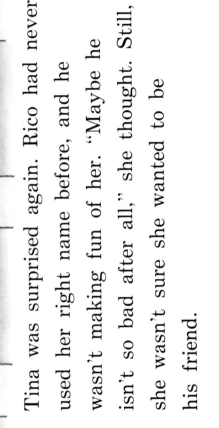

Tina was surprised again. Rico had never used her right name before, and he wasn't making fun of her. "Maybe he isn't so bad after all," she thought. Still, she wasn't sure she wanted to be his friend.

"My mother is waiting for me," she said. "I'll stop and play with your kitten some other time."

As she walked home, no one called "Tall Tina!" or "String Bean Tina!" That felt good.

77

Tina Runs to Win

A week went by. No one said anything about how tall Tina was. She began to walk straight again.

A warm spring day came, and the children were on the playground. Mr. Peters, one of the teachers, called, "We're going to have races. Rico will be the captain of one team. Kate will be the captain of the other team. Captains, pick your team!"

Kate wanted Joshua for her team. Then Rico had to pick someone.

"I take you!" he said, pointing to Tina.

ready
set go!

"Why should I be on his team?" Tina asked herself. But she walked slowly over to Rico.

Everyone got on one line or the other. The tall children went to the back of each line. Joshua was the last one on Kate's team. Tina was the last on Rico's team.

"Ready, set, GO!" called Mr. Peters.

79

Off Kate and Rico ran to the fence, and back to the next ones in line. Both teams were fast. It was a close race right to the very end.

"Run, Tina, run!" shouted Rico. Tina ran as hard as she could—she had to win. Tina's long legs took her over the line just before Joshua. She had done it! She had won for her team! Everyone shouted. Tina could hear Rico shouting with them. Rico gave Tina a big smile.

That night, when Tina looked at herself, she saw a girl who was straight and tall. She didn't bend her back or her legs. She felt like herself again, happy to be in a tall family.

Words

Some words describe people. They tell how people look, how they feel, and how they act. Words can describe <u>you</u>.

Think about how you look.

Are you tall or short? Big or small?

Is your skin light or dark?

What color is your hair?

Is your hair straight or curly?

What color are your eyes?

Do you feel happy most of the time?

When do you feel sad?

82

Describe You

Do you ever feel worried?

Silly? Angry? Excited?

Do you talk a lot or are you shy?

Are you noisy or quiet?

Is your voice soft or loud?

Are you kind and thoughtful?

Are you friendly? Funny? Forgetful?

Can you write about yourself? Use describing words that tell about how you look, how you feel, and how you act. You may want to use some of the words on these pages.

THE KNEE-HIGH MAN
Julius Lester

Once there was a knee-high man. He was no taller than a man's knee. Because he was so tiny, he was very sad. He wanted to be big like everyone else.

One day he decided to go see Mr. Horse. "Mr. Horse, how can I get big like you?" he asked.

Mr. Horse said, "Well, eat a lot of corn. Then run around a lot. Soon you'll be as big as me."

So the knee-high man ate so much corn that his stomach hurt. Then he ran and ran until his legs hurt. But he didn't get any bigger. So he decided that Mr. Horse had been wrong.

He decided to go ask Mr. Bull.
"Mr. Bull, how can I get big like you?"

Mr. Bull said, "Eat a lot of grass.
Then yell and yell as loud as you can.
Soon you'll be as big as me."

So the knee-high man ate so much
grass that his stomach hurt. He yelled
so much that his throat hurt. But he
didn't get any bigger. So he decided
that Mr. Bull was all wrong, too.

Now he didn't know who else to ask.
One night he saw Mr. Hoot Owl, and
he remembered that Mr. Owl knew
everything.

"Mr. Owl, how can I get big like Mr. Horse and Mr. Bull?"

"What do you want to be big for?" Mr. Hoot Owl asked.

"I want to be big so that when I get into a fight, I can beat everyone."

Mr. Hoot Owl hooted. "Anyone ever try to pick a fight with you?"

The knee-high man thought. "Well, now that you ask, no one ever did."

Mr. Owl said, "Then, if you don't have to fight anyone, you don't have to be bigger than you are."

"But Mr. Owl," the knee-high man said, "I want to be big so I can see far ahead of me."

Mr. Hoot Owl hooted. "If you climb a tall tree, you can see far ahead."

"I didn't think of that," said the knee-high man.

Mr. Hoot Owl hooted again. "That's what's wrong, Mr. Knee-High Man. You haven't done any thinking at all. I'm smaller than you, and you don't see me thinking about being big. Mr. Knee-High Man, you wanted something that you don't need."

And the knee-high man knew that Mr. Owl was right.

Who Am I?

The trees ask me,
And the sky,
And the sea asks me
    Who am I?
The grass asks me,
And the sand,
And the rocks ask me
    Who I am.

The wind tells me
At nightfall,
And the rain tells me
Someone small.
Someone small
Someone small
But a piece
of
it
all.

—Felice Holman

Gordon the Goat

Munro Leaf

Gordon was a goat. He lived on a ranch in Texas. Gordon liked to eat. He didn't care what he ate. He would eat anything. Most of the time he ate leaves from the trees that grew around the ranch. But he was just as happy with an old rag, or some ham—if he could get it.

And every now and then Gordon would start to eat a cactus. But he was sorry every time he did!

Gordon lived on the ranch with a lot of other goats. He didn't work very hard. All Gordon did was go on being Gordon day after day. And now and then he would get his hair cut.

Gordon had very soft hair. The men who cut it called it mohair. They sold the mohair to other people. The people used the mohair to make coats and other very soft things. That was all right with Gordon. He didn't care what the men did with his hair; just so they didn't nick him when they cut it off.

Some of the goats on the ranch were called lead goats. The other goats always walked behind and went every place the lead goats went.

When a lead goat got tired of staying in one place, he would go to another place. All the other goats would tag along behind him.

Sometimes a new place was better than an old place. And sometimes it was not as good. But, better or not, when the lead goat went, all the rest of the goats went along.

Gordon went, too. He didn't know why. He just did what all the rest of the goats did. He didn't really think about it.

But it took Gordon so long to get going that all the other goats were ahead of him. Gordon was always at the tail end of the line.

One hot day, the lead goat got tired of staying where he was, so he started out to find another place. He remembered seeing some new weeds on the other side of a hill. Off he went to find the new weeds. The rest of the goats were right behind him— with Gordon at the tail end of the line.

The Twister

After a long, hot walk, the goats found the new weeds. Gordon ate some. The weeds were not very good, and soon Gordon didn't feel very well. He was sorry he had come along. Gordon sat down on the side of the hill. He decided to stay there until he felt better. But just when Gordon was starting to feel a little better, the lead goat went off to look for another place.

Away he went, and the other goats followed him. The very last goat was Gordon, who really didn't feel like going at all.

94

Gordon walked and walked. The hot sun beat down on him. And Gordon began to ask himself why he was going along. Why didn't he do some thinking for himself? Why had he followed all the other goats, who were following the lead goat just because that was what they always did? It all seemed very silly to Gordon.

Then he saw something way off, ahead of all the goats. It was a big, dark-looking thing. And it was coming right at them. It began right on the ground and it went right up into the sky. Gordon had never seen anything as big before.

The thing was coming at them,
faster and faster. Gordon wished that
the lead goat would turn around and go
another way. But the lead goat went on
walking straight ahead. And so the other
goats went on walking straight ahead, too.

The thing was coming straight at
them until all the goats were right in
the middle of it. It was a twister. Now
a twister is no fun to be in, and Gordon
was scared. Up he flew into the middle
of a black cloud. It threw him around
and around. It threw him upside down
and downside up.

Now Gordon was really sorry that he ever ate the new weeds. First he turned yellow, and then he turned green. And then he was sick. Gordon was very sorry for himself. He was never so sorry for himself before.

When he thought that he couldn't last much longer, he saw the old lead goat go flying past him. The old goat went higher and higher. He looked as if he was even sicker than Gordon.

97

Just then Gordon blew out of the twister. He fell with a bang in the middle of some grass. The grass was soft so he didn't break anything, but still it hurt a lot.

After a long time, Gordon got up. He hurt all over. But Gordon knew something now that he would always remember.

Never again would he follow along just because all the other goats did. He was going to find out first—
where he was going,
why he was going, and
what he was going to do
when he got there!

Gordon does his own thinking now. He gets along much better than before.

99

UPI

Pittsburgh Athletic Company Inc.

UPI

Roberto Clemente:
The Star From Puerto Rico

Elizabeth Levy

It was the summer of 1971. Everyone who liked baseball was watching the World Series. Who would win? Not many people thought the Pittsburgh Pirates could win. Only a few fans thought the Pirates could do it. But, by the end of the Series, the Pirates were the winners! How did they do it? They had a star named Roberto Clemente.

Roberto Clemente grew up in Puerto Rico. He always wanted to be a great baseball player. His father thought Roberto should do something better than play baseball. But Roberto didn't give up. He worked hard to become a good ball player. Each year he got better and better.

Soon after he got out of school, Roberto Clemente was asked to join the Pittsburgh

Photo by Les Banos

UPI

UPI

UPI

Pirates. Once he joined the Pirates, Clemente wanted to show the world that a Puerto Rican could be the best baseball player there was.

It was not always easy for Roberto Clemente to keep playing baseball. In Puerto Rico, his back had been badly hurt when he was hit by a car. One time when he was playing for the Pirates, a ball hit him and hurt his arm. For most of his life, his back and his arm hurt every time he played ball.

But Clemente wouldn't let anything stop him from playing. He had very strong arms and strong hands. He could hit and throw a baseball very well. As the years went by, he became a star player. One year he was named the best player in the league. Four times he was the best batter in the league.

When Roberto Clemente first joined the Pittsburgh Pirates, they were in the last place in their league. But with Clemente's help, they started to win.

In 1971 the Pirates did so well that they got to play in the World Series. Clemente was already a star. But he still wanted to show the whole world that he was the very best player of all.

In the seven games of the World Series, Clemente got on base more than four times out of ten. Nobody did better. He walked up to the plate with his special long bat in his hands. He hit at just about any ball. And nobody did better than Roberto when the Pirates were out in the field. He jumped to catch fly balls as if he had wings. The balls he threw into home plate from the field put many runners out.

The World Series was over. Clemente was the biggest star on the team. He was very happy. He had shown the world that a Puerto Rican was the best in baseball. Roberto Clemente had made Puerto Ricans very proud.

Every winter Roberto went back home
to Puerto Rico. He loved his homeland and
its people. He wanted to help them as much
as he could.

Many times he would be very tired.
All he wanted to do was rest at home
with his wife and sons. But if anyone
asked him for help, he would always say yes.
He went to schools to play baseball
with children. He helped many young
Puerto Rican baseball players get a start.

Then in 1972, there was an earthquake in Nicaragua. Many people died, and many more were hurt. Many houses fell down. Many children lost their mothers and fathers in the earthquake. The people in Nicaragua needed help very badly. Roberto got a call for help. At once, he collected a lot of food and money. Then he decided to fly to Nicaragua. He wanted to take the food and money there himself.

UPI

The plane that was taking Roberto Clemente to Nicaragua went down in the ocean. Roberto died. Baseball fans everywhere felt very sad. The whole Pittsburgh Pirate team flew down to Puerto Rico. They wanted to be with Roberto's family. People all over the country said he was not only a great baseball player, but also a very great man. But the people in Puerto Rico felt saddest of all. Roberto Clemente had made them very proud. To them he was a great Puerto Rican.

107

Biography

A biography is a story about someone's life.
The word *biography* comes from words people used
long ago—*bios* and *graphein. Bios* means
life and *graphein* means to write.
Write a life!

You can write a biography. Get together with
someone in your class.
Find out all about her or him.
Then write!
To help you, here are some things you may
ask your friend.

What is your full name?

Do you have a nickname?

When is your birthday?

Where do you live?

Who is in your family?

Do you have a pet?

What do you like to do?

What is the most important thing you have done?

What can you remember about when you were little?

What do you want to be when you grow up?

Get together.

The Fastest Quitter in Town

Phyllis Green

Crack! The boy at bat hit a grounder. A boy in the field got the ball and threw it to Johnny at first base. Johnny thought he had it, but the only thing he got in his glove was...air!

Johnny threw down his glove in disgust. "I quit," he said.

"You always quit when things don't go right," everyone yelled. "Why don't you learn to catch?"

"I can catch. Old Greenly can't throw," Johnny yelled back.

"Come on. Let's play without him. We don't need him," the boys said.

Johnny picked up his glove and ran off the field. When the boys couldn't see him any more, he sat down and cried. He had told himself he would play the whole game today, but he had quit right at the start. If only old Greenly could throw a ball right. If only he had not quit right away. Now they would never let him back in the game.

Johnny decided to go and see his great-grandfather. He would tell him all about Greenly's bad throw.

Great-Grandfather lived in the house next door to Johnny's house. He lived with Johnny's grandfather and grandmother. Great-Grandfather was very old. He could not see too well any more, but he was a lot of fun to be with.

When Johnny got there, the first thing Great-Grandfather said was, "Short game, today?"

Johnny didn't say anything.

"I thought you were going to play the whole game today. Something go wrong?" asked Great-Grandfather. "Why don't you get some cookies and then tell me about the game?"

Johnny got some cookies in the kitchen. When he came back, he said, "Greenly thinks he's so hot. Only he never learned to throw a ball."

"That so?" said Great-Grandfather. "He's that bad?"

"He's not really bad," said Johnny. "He just throws a little high."

"A little high for you," said Great-Grandfather.

"Yes," said Johnny.

"Is that why you quit? Because you missed the ball?" asked Great-Grandfather.

"Well, kind of," said Johnny. "But tomorrow I'm going to play the whole game."

Great-Grandfather looked at Johnny. "Tomorrow you'll catch the ball," he said. "But Johnny, even if you don't, don't give up. Stay on the field. It's only a game. You should have fun even if you don't catch the ball."

The Lost Ring

The next afternoon Johnny took his glove and walked over to the playground.

"Oh, no," the boys said. "Here comes the fastest quitter in town."

Johnny waited by the side of the field and watched the boys play. Then Greenly called, "Oh, all right, Johnny. We'll let you play. Are you going to play the whole game today?"

"Yes, I am," said Johnny.

"Then get out there and play."

When it was Johnny's turn at bat, he hit the ball way out. It looked like a homer. He ran fast. As he ran, Johnny saw Greenly throwing the ball to the catcher. Johnny ran to home base. He was sure he was safe.

Then everyone yelled, "Out!"

"I'm safe! I'm safe!" Johnny yelled.

"You're out!" they yelled back.

Johnny didn't want to say anything, but the words just came right out. "I quit."

Everyone was disgusted. "This is it for you, Johnny. You're the fastest quitter in town! Don't come around ever again."

"The fastest quitter," said Johnny to himself as he walked away.

Johnny went right over to see his Great-Grandfather. What would he tell him this time? When he got there, Johnny saw Great-Grandfather sitting in his chair. But he was surprised to see Great-Grandfather looking very sad. Johnny decided not to tell him anything about the game that day.

"Oh, Johnny," said Great-Grandfather. "I need your help. You know my special gold ring—the one I got when I was a boy? Well, I lost it."

"I'll help you find it," said Johnny. "Where do you think you lost it?"

"I don't know," said Great-Grandfather.

Johnny looked everywhere in the house. He looked in Great-Grandfather's chair and in his bed. He looked in all the rooms. But he didn't find the lost ring. Great-Grandfather was very sad. He did not move from his chair. "I have to find that ring," he said. "I have always had it on my finger."

"Please don't worry, Great-Grandfather. You'll get your ring back. I'll never stop looking for it," said Johnny.

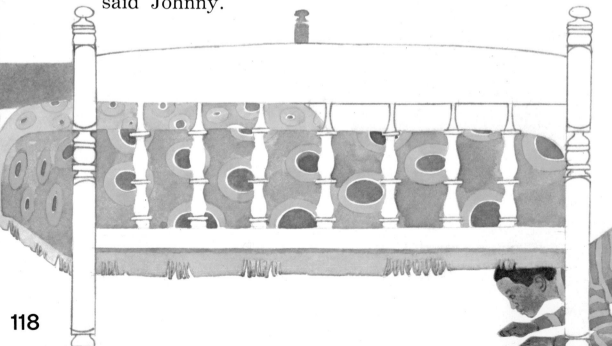

Johnny went over to Great-Grandfather's house the next day and the next. He looked and looked everywhere for the ring. But he couldn't find it.

Each day Great-Grandfather was sadder and quieter. Johnny's grandmother and grandfather began to worry about him. They didn't know what to do.

Then Johnny's grandmother had an idea. "Johnny, I have a ring that looks just like Great-Grandfather's ring. Give him this ring and tell him it's his gold ring."

"But I can't do that," Johnny said. "He'll know. He's smarter than you think. He wants the ring he lost."

"We only want to help Great-Grandfather feel happy again," said his grandmother.

"Oh, all right. I'll give it to him,"
Johnny said. "But I'm sure he'll know."
Johnny went into Great-Grandfather's
room and closed the door. He put the
ring in Great-Grandfather's hand.

"Johnny, that's not my ring," said
Great-Grandfather.

"I know, Great-Grandfather. But I
want you to pretend. Grandmother wants
you to think that this is your ring so
you won't worry so much. Please pretend.
I'll never stop looking for your ring.
Never."

"Really, Johnny? You won't quit?
All right. I'll pretend," said
Great-Grandfather.

Johnny Doesn't Quit

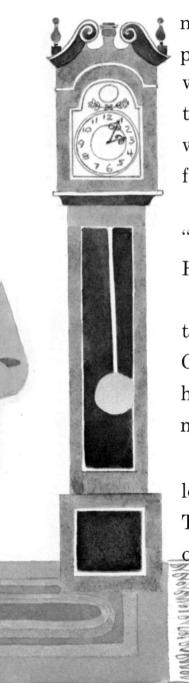

For a long time, Johnny didn't go near the playground when the boys were playing ball. Every day after school, he went over to Great-Grandfather's house to look for the lost ring. Many days went by, but Johnny still could not find the ring.

One day Great-Grandfather said, "Johnny, I feel like a little sun today. Help me out to the porch, will you?"

They sat on the porch together, near the yard in back of the house. Great-Grandfather touched the ring on his finger. "Are you still looking for my lost ring, Johnny?"

"Yes, Great-Grandfather, I'm still looking. Please don't give up on me." Then Johnny asked, "Were you out here on the porch the day you lost your ring?"

"I don't know. It's hard to remember," said Great-Grandfather. "But sometimes, when I'm out here, I like to walk in the yard and touch the flowers. I can't see them too well, so I like to touch them."

Johnny had an idea. He ran to the flowers in the yard. He got down on the ground, and began to feel around with his hands. Then he saw something bright. "Oh, please, please, let it be the ring," he thought. He picked up something gold.

"Great-Grandfather,
Great-Grandfather!" he yelled.
"I found it! I found it!"

Johnny ran with the ring to
Great-Grandfather. Great-Grandfather took
the ring and hugged Johnny again and
again. Johnny was very happy. He had
such a good feeling inside. He had not
quit this time. They went in to tell
Grandmother. She put some tape on the
ring so it would not fall off
Great-Grandfather's finger again.

The next day Johnny went over to the playground. The boys all laughed when they saw him. "Well, look who's here," they said.

"Can I be in the game?" Johnny asked.

The boy at bat called, "I say **no**! He was kicked out for good."

Other boys yelled, "No! He's a quitter."

But then Greenly yelled, "You know we need another player. Get out there, Johnny."

Johnny ran out to take his place in the game. This time he was sure he would not quit. And he didn't. He played the whole game.

It was late that afternoon when Johnny went to see Great-Grandfather.

"Where have you been, Johnny? You're late today. I thought you forgot about me," said Great-Grandfather.

"I was playing baseball," said Johnny. "Great-Grandfather, remember when I was a quitter? Remember when I wouldn't play the whole game? Well, today I didn't quit, and I feel great."

"You, a quitter?" said Great-Grandfather. "I don't remember that at all. That just doesn't seem like you, Johnny."

Johnny took the old man's hand and together they walked out to the yard to look at the flowers.

WORD LIST

The new words introduced in this book are listed below beside the page number on which they first appear. The children should be able to independently identify italicized words at this level.

6. impossible
   possum
   Randolph
   understand
   possums
   hang
   upside
   sadly
   sighed
   onto
   wound
7. *Eugene*
   Geraldine
   Randolph's
   first
   dear
8. *flop*
   kindly
   trying
   pile
9. *falls*
   brothers
10. *hanging*
11. *sap*
    woke
    jumping
    pull
    leaf
    paw
    stuck

12. *picking*
    stick
    held
    paws
    sticking
    hung
13. unwind
    nap
14. *dries*
    rub
16. trick
    wonderful
17. *tricky*
    jolly
    louder
21. *players*
    page
    royal
    tailor
    tailor's
    son
    soldier
22. dining
    palace
    supper
    sighs
23. *bring*
    brings
24. kitchen
    tastes

   salt
25. *king's*
    apron
26. sandwich
    ham
28. poor
29. *meat*
    sell
30. *line*
31. *cook's*
32. majesty
    tries
    tasty
33. *undercooked*
    overcooked
    laughs
    son's
34. *everyday*
    potato
35. *send*
37. *whatever*
    bean
    rice
40. share
    Anita
    quietly
    listened
    shared
    clapped
    dolls

126

toy
Monday
Anita's
41. heard
42. Paco
dinner
store
43. tomorrow
whole
47. wow
toys
Mexico
picked
48. balero
haven't
almost
49. classroom
bright
sharing
Mexican
Perez
50. baleros
hangs
string
flip
51. piggy bank
52. piggy banks
donkeys
coyotes
57. grows
soil
minerals
sunlight
tree's
roots
countryside

58. pavement
buildings
59. ailanthus
pavements
building
bit
enough
60. red-brown
seed
wing-like
wherever
cracks
64. Tina
taller
pocketbook
shelf
65. Tina's
Maria
schoolgirls
66. Miss
67. seat
row
69. legs
floor
70. short
72. standing
straight
aren't
73. stand
fence
peeked
74. crybaby
75. handkerchief
Rico's
78. win
Peters
teachers

we're
races
team
captains
79. Kate's
set
80. both
teams
race
shouted
won
shouting
81. bend
84. knee-high
man's
knee
else
corn
stomach
bigger
wrong
85. bull
throat
hoot
owl
86. fight
beat
hooted
87. climb
90. Gordon
goat
ranch
Texas
rag
cactus
91. goats
mohair

sold

nick

92. *lead*

    staying

    tag

93. *weeds*

94. twister

    starting

    followed

95. *following*

    seemed

    dark-looking

    sky

96. middle

    cloud

    downside

97. *longer*

    past

    higher

    sicker

98. *blew*

    bang

99. *follow*

100. *Roberto*

    Clemente

    star

    World Series

    Pittsburgh

    pirates

fans

winners

player

103. *Puerto Rican*

    easy

    arm

    league

    batter

    Clemente's

    already

104. *base*

    nobody

    plate

    bat

    field

    runners

    biggest

    shown

    Puerto Ricans

105. *homeland*

    sons

    schools

107. earthquake

    Nicaragua

    collected

    plane

    pirate

    Roberto's

    saddest

110. *fastest*

    quitter

    crack

    grounder

    Johnny

    glove

    disgust

    quit.

    learn

    Greenly

111. *great-grandfather*

    Greenly's

112. Johnny's

    grandfather

113. *throws*

115. *ring*

116. *homer*

    throwing

    catcher

    safe

117. chair

118. *great-grandfather's*

    rooms

    worry

119. *sadder*

    smarter

121. porch

    yard

    touched

122. *touch*